Grandparents

A Gift of Memories

© 1997 Havoc Publishing

ISBN 1-57977-118-1

Published and created by Havoc Publishing

San Diego, California

First Printing, October 1997

Designed by Juddesign

Made in China

Please write to us for more information on our

Havoc Publishing Record Books and Products.

HAVOC PUBLISHING

7868 Silverton Avenue, Suite A

San Diego, California 92126

Grandparents

A Gift of Memories

Contents

Contents

Photo

All About Us

Grandmother

Full name

I´m named after

My birth date

My birth place

Grandfather

Full name

I´m named after

My birth date

My birth place

Our Family Tree

Grandmother

Great Great Grandmother

Great Great Grandfather

Great Great Grandfather

Great Great Grandmother

Great Grandmother

Great Grandfather

Grandmother

Grandfather

Great Great Grandfather

Great Great Grandmother

Great Great Grandmother

Great Great Grandfather

Great Grandmother

Great Grandfather

Grandfather

Grandmother's Family History

When my family came to this country

Where they came from

Where they settled

Where they worked

Grandfather's Family History

When my family came to this country

_____

_____

_____

Where they came from

_____

_____

_____

Where they settled

_____

_____

_____

Where they worked

_____

_____

_____

_____

_____

Ancestral Stories

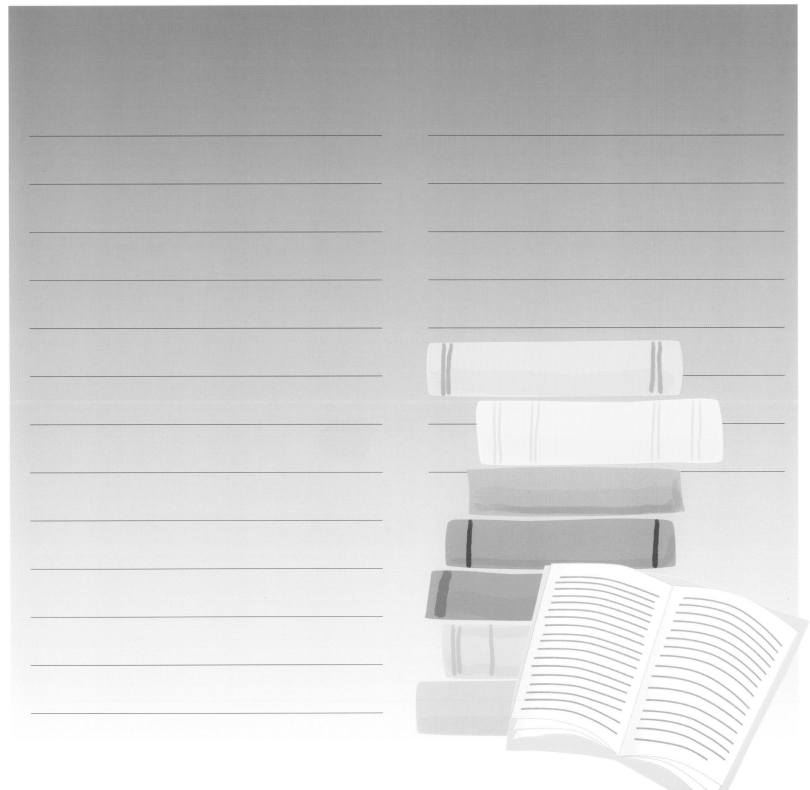

Photograph

Grandmother's Early Days

Where I grew up

What I was like as a child

Some of my childhood favorites

My earliest memories

Favorite places

Favorite toy

Favorite games

Grandfather's Early Days

Where I grew up

_____

_____

_____

What I was like as a child

_____

_____

_____

Some of my childhood favorites

_____

_____

_____

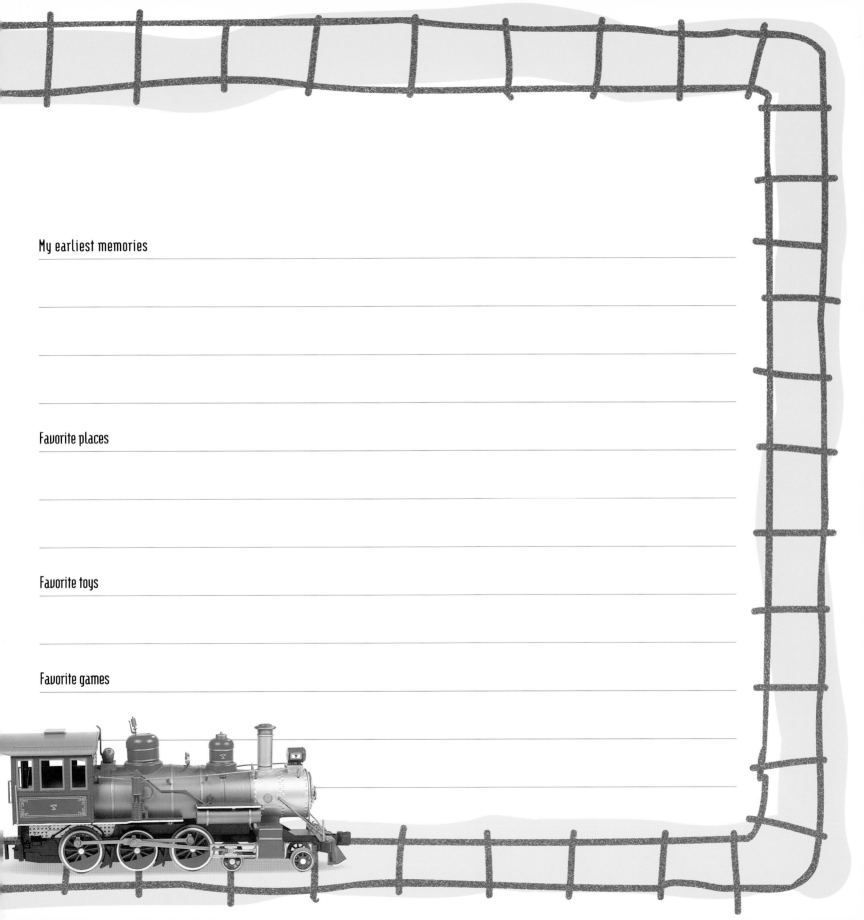

My earliest memories

Favorite places

Favorite toys

Favorite games

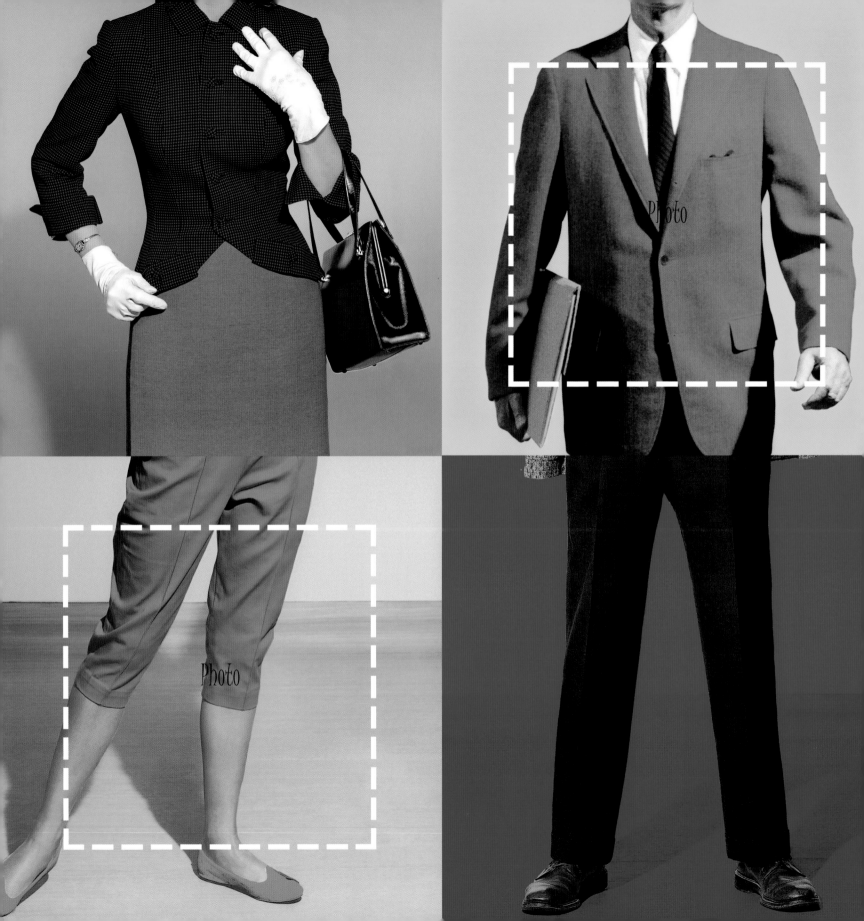

In Our Day

Fads
_____
_____
_____

Trends
_____
_____
_____

Fashions
_____
_____
_____

What we did for entertainment
_____
_____

Costs in Our Day

Candy bar
_____

Movie ticket
_____

Postage stamp
_____

Gallon of gas
_____

Gallon of milk
_____

Loaf of bread
_____

Haircut

World leaders

Famous scandals

Important issues

National issues

Local issues

How the World Was

Photo

Photo

When We Were Young

Favorite movie stars

Changes in music

Favorite radio shows

Inventions & Firsts

Inventions during our lifetime

Inventions that affected our lives the most

The most amazing invention

Our favorite inventions

What we remember about our first television

_____

_____

_____

Photo

What we remember about our first radio

_____

_____

What we remember about our first telephone

_____

_____

The First Time

When & where we first met each other

_____

_____

_____

_____

The courtship

_____

_____

_____

When & where we became engaged

_____

_____

_____

_____

We Met

What we enjoy doing together

_____

_____

_____

_____

Favorite things about each other

_____

_____

_____

_____

A funny story

_____

_____

_____

_____

Wedding Bells

Date
_____

Place
_____

Time
_____

We celebrated by
_____

_____

_____

Grandmother wore
_____

_____

Cherished gifts
_____

_____

_____

_____

Photo

Photo

Memorable wedding stories

Our First Year

Where we lived

_____

_____

Grandfather's job

_____

_____

_____

_____

Grandmother's job

_____

_____

What we enjoyed

_____

_____

_____

_____

_____

WELCOME

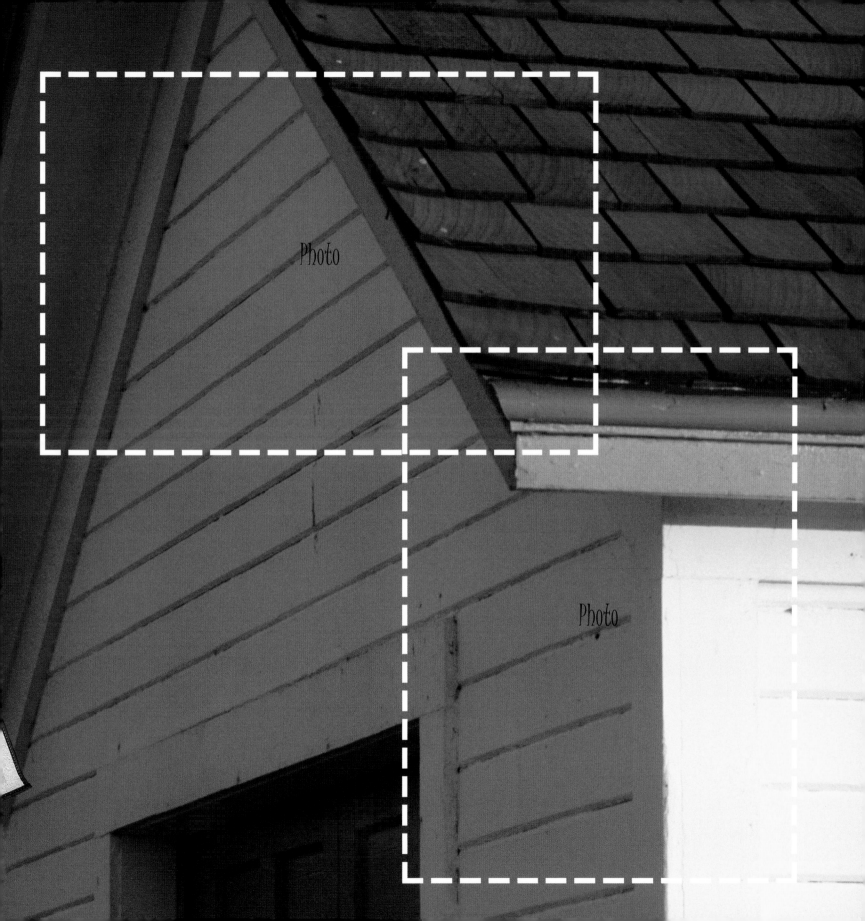

Photograph

We're Parents!

Your mom/dad was born on

_____

at

_____

Time/place

_____

We decided on the name

_____

because

_____

_____

Important facts

_____

_____

_____

Other children we had

_____

_____

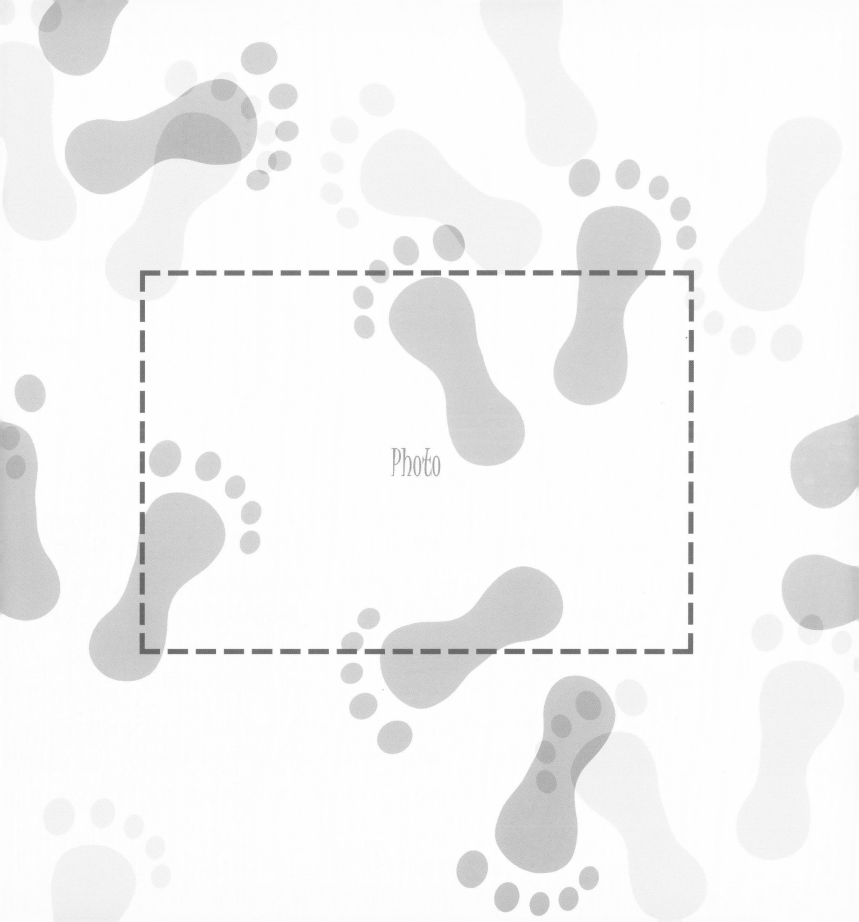

Photo

Our Life as Parents

Some of our fondest memories

The funniest thing we remember

What your mom/dad was like growing up

Things never change

When your parents met

_____

_____

_____

_____

_____

About their wedding day

_____

_____

_____

_____

Our favorite memories of your parents

_____

_____

_____

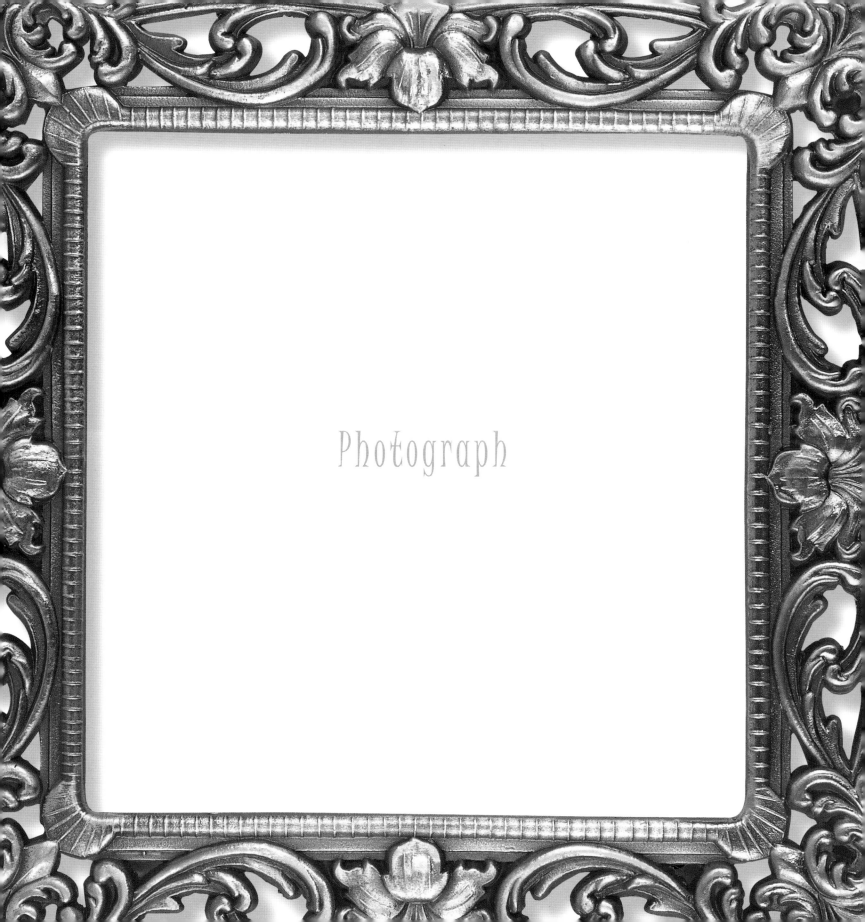

Becoming Grandparents

When we heard the happy news

_____

_____

When we first saw you

_____

_____

Things we shared with you

_____

_____

Funny things you did

Your favorite toy

Our favorite thing about you

Fond Memories as Grandparents

One of the funniest things we remember

_____

_____

_____

_____

Favorite times spent with you

_____

_____

_____

_____

Our Friendships

Our best friends today

How we spend time together

Friends we'd love to see more often

Grandfather´s most memorable friendships

_____

_____

_____

_____

_____

_____

_____

_____

_____

_____

Grandmother´s most memorable friendships

_____

_____

_____

_____

_____

_____

Our Favorite Things

Grandmother

Music _____

TV shows _____

Season _____

Hobbies _____

_____

_____

_____

_____

_____

_____

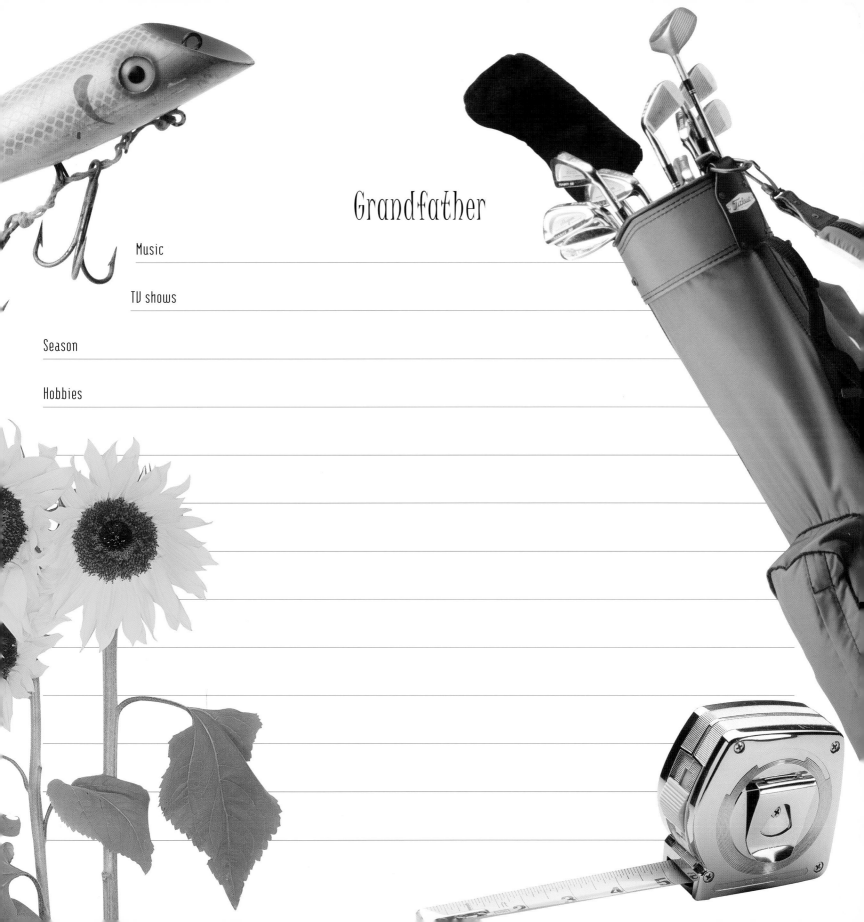

Grandfather

Music _____

TV shows _____

Season _____

Hobbies _____

Family Recipes

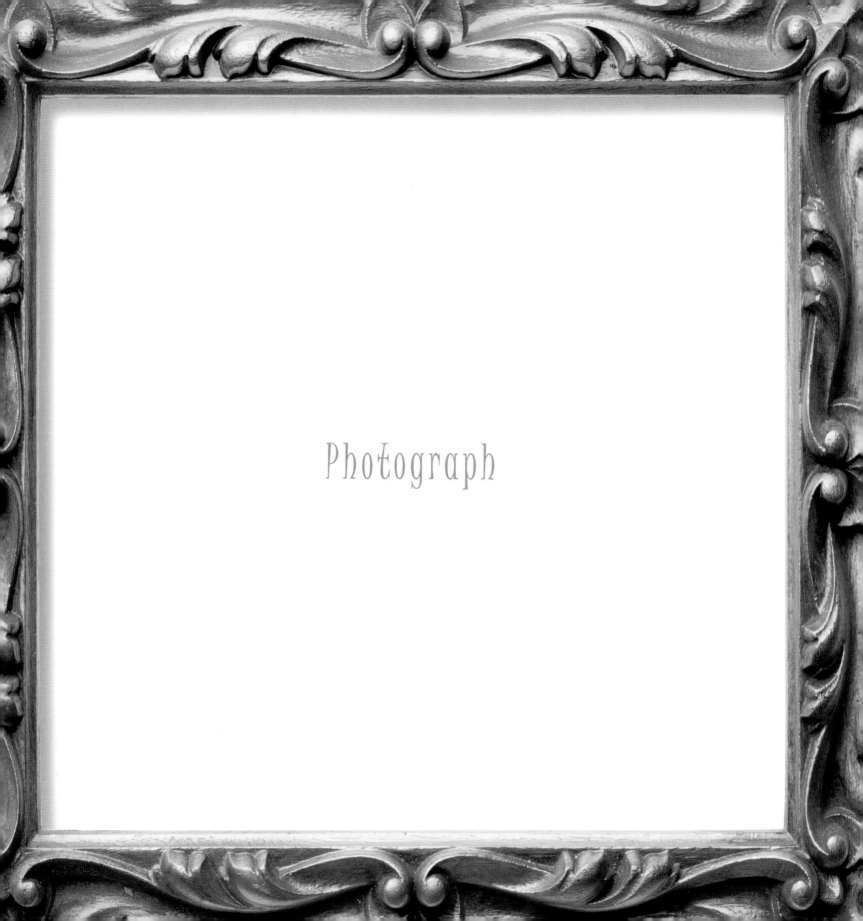

Family Time

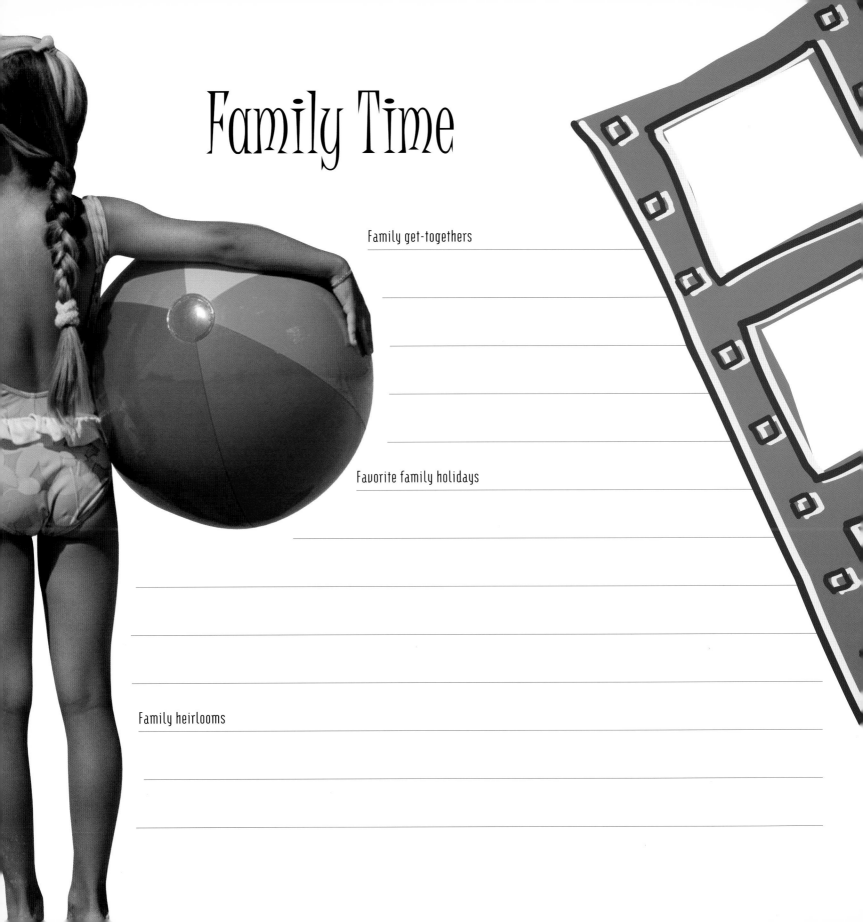

Family get-togethers

_____

_____

_____

Favorite family holidays

_____

_____

_____

Family heirlooms

_____

_____

Priceless family stories

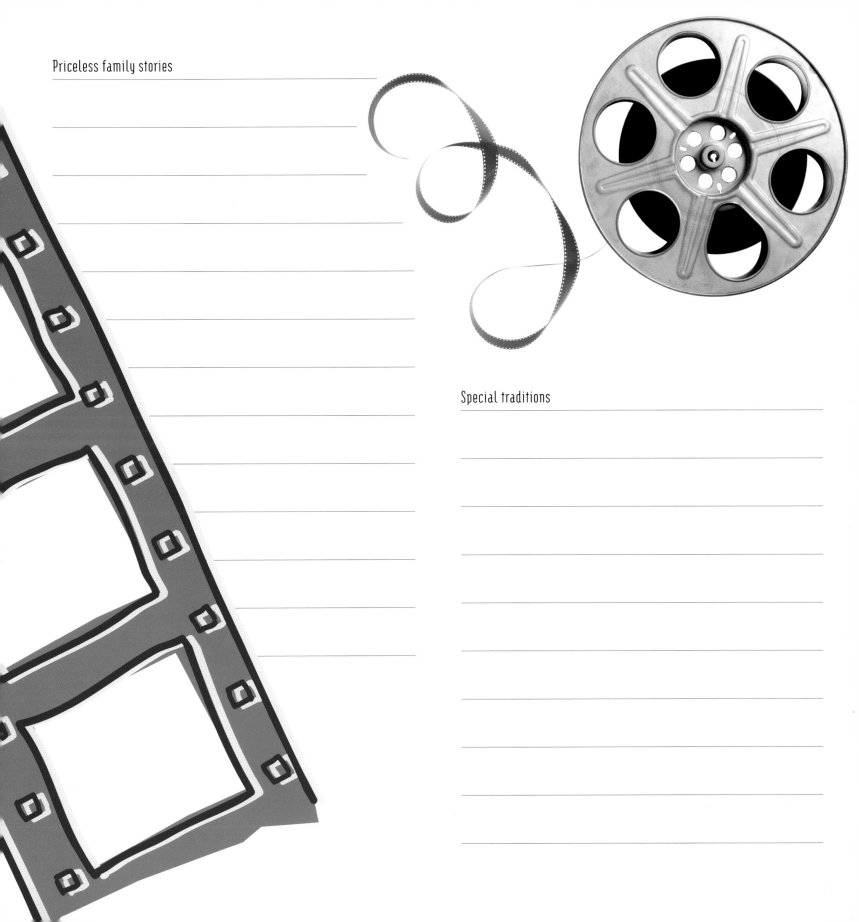

Special traditions

Our Travels

Different places we've traveled to

_____

_____

_____

_____

Some of our favorite places

_____

_____

_____

_____

_____

Parks, landmarks, theatres & museums

_____

_____

_____

_____

_____

_____

_____

_____

Photo

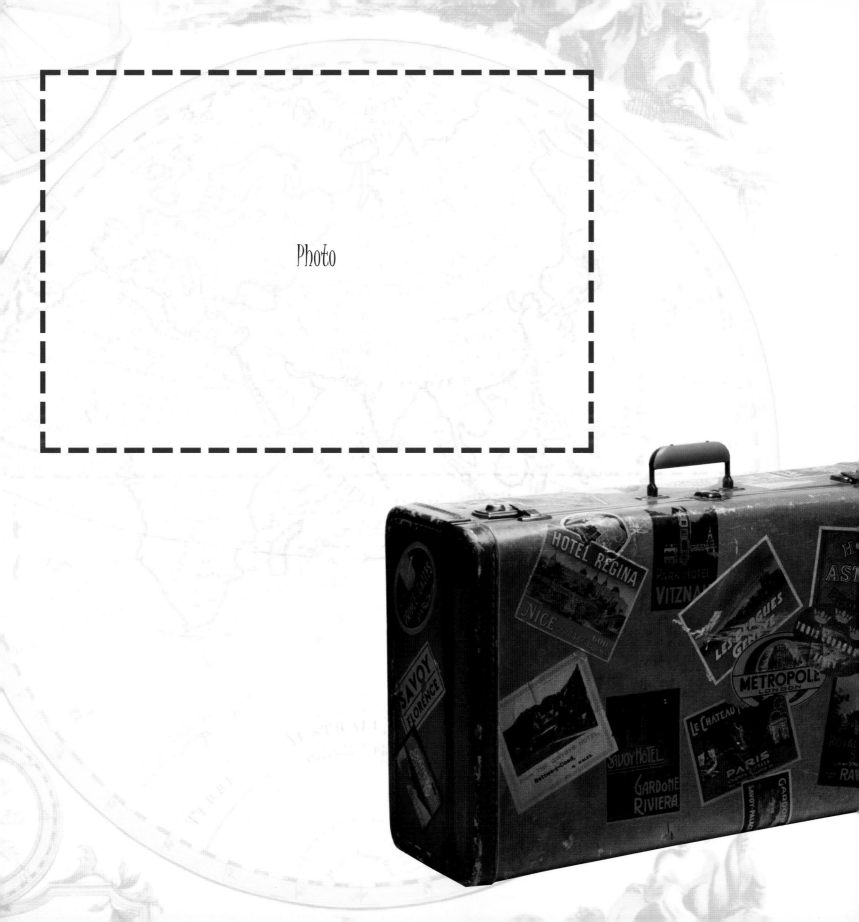

Keepsakes & Mementos

Memento

Photo

Photo

From the Heart

Available Record Books from Havoc

Baby	Mothers & Daughters
Coach	My Pregnancy
College Life	Our Honeymoon
Couples	Retirement
Dad	School Days
Girlfriends	Single Life
Golf	Sisters
Grandmother	Teacher
Grandparents	Traveling Adventures
Mom	Tying The Knot

Please write to us with your ideas for additional
Havoc Publishing Record Books and Products

HAVOC PUBLISHING
7868 Silverton Avenue, Suite A
San Diego, California 92126